Biff and Chip played on the sand.

Dad went to sleep.

Biff and Chip put sand on Dad.

They made a sandcastle.

They put Dad's hat on top.

They went to get an ice cream.

Dad was still asleep.

Chip looked at the donkeys.

Biff looked at the boat.

They looked at the go-karts.

They looked at Dad's hat.

"Oh no!" said Biff.

Dad was hiding.

Biff was cross.

The hat was on a stick.